DID YOU KNOW?

For parents and children accustomed to long, time-consuming tests, it may seem impossible to truly gather sufficient placement information with just a few questions. But, the truth is that you can easily and effectively learn where to place your child academically in a subject with just twenty simple questions!

How is this possible? Well, keep in mind that most achievement tests are administered to large groups of students, and the results are processed through computers. Therefore, these tests require a minimum of three to five questions per topic in order to assess an average.

When a test is administered one on one and the parent walks through each question with their child, however, the assessment results are not strictly based on right or wrong answers. Instead, they are based on observation of thought processes, understanding of the question, and the ability to work through the question or problem. As a result, typically only one question, combined with interactive administration of the test, is required to adequately assess a child's level of understanding.

Well Planned Start includes both the administrator guide and step-by-step answer key in order for parents to confidently administer, observe, and evaluate the test-taking process to understand exactly where their children place.

Contents

A TOOL FOR PARENTS

As a mom of five, I began giving my kids achievement tests at an early age. After teaching them how to fill in the small circles and sharpen their number 2 pencils, the kids would walk into classrooms, doors would close, and testing would begin. Six weeks later, I would receive test reports which gave vague indications of how each child was doing compared to children across the nation. The broad descriptions of achievement in specific areas provided very little useful information to help me know how to strengthen my kids in the coming year.

Over the years, I sought an assessment option that would help me choose the best curriculum, cover information unknown to my child, and fill in any educational gaps. Unfortunately, none of the tests I found accomplished this goal. That needed to change!

Recognizing the need, I began working with the Well Planned Gal curriculum developer **Tiffany Orthman, M.Ed.** to develop a one-of-a-kind, easy-to-use assessment and placement test for parents and children to work through together.

Well Planned Start is unique as it guides you, the parent, to a better understanding of what your child knows, comprehends, and can process correctly. This educational evaluation tool offers a two-sided assessment. First, you will find a parent assessment, helping you discover what you know about your child. Second, a student placement test walks your child through a series of questions while you follow along with an administrator guide that helps you know how to process your child's answers and thinking processes.

Best of all, I've included helpful tips for each of the subjects and areas, as well as a checklist of milestones for this school year. Milestones work as a guide as you watch your child develop emotionally, physically, and educationally throughout the year.

As you proceed through this book and into your school year, remember these five key points:

- Relax! This is not a comparison or a judgment game. This is a tool to help you determine where your child is.

- Use the information to make improvements. Spend extra time or use a different approach where there are weaknesses. Offer more activities if you need to challenge your child. If you have not covered an area, now is the time!

- Try to set aside presuppositions as you begin the assessment. Remember, dislike for a subject does not indicate a weakness.

- These assessments are based on grasping concepts rather than parroting correct answers.

- Bible has been added as an additional component in these assessments. Keep in mind, though, that spiritual growth is not based on age. This is simply a resource to help you have an idea of where to look for and encourage growth.

Rebecca Farris
WELL PLANNED GAL

BOOK OVERVIEW

The Well Planned Start has been organized and arranged in order of sequence. Each section has an introduction with detailed information on how to assess your child, administer the placement test, and understand the milestones.

PARENT ASSESSMENT TESTS

The goal of this section is to become familiar with what your child knows. If your child has been attending school or hybrid homeschooling, this area will give you the opportunity to begin dialogues to understand the depth of understanding in each subject.

There are detailed instructions on how to use this assessment, as well as worksheets to journal your findings. At the end of this section, we give practical teaching tips to help you enhance each subject area.

STUDENT PLACEMENT TESTS

Unlike standardized testing, these placement tests allow parents to see first hand the specific areas children excel and need help in. By using the guide to administer the tests, you not only give instructions to your child, but you will also follow instructions that help you know what to watch for as the child works through the questions. This allows you to discover where the breakdown begins in the process.

PARENT TEACHING TIPS

After administering tests, you will find practical teaching tips and activity suggestions for every concept covered in the placement test. Use these suggested activities to strengthen low-scoring areas, keep your child challenged, fill in gaps, and more!

3RD GRADE MILESTONES

Complete with a checklist of milestones, Well Planned Start provides a year-long guide on what to expect from your child physically, emotionally, and academically. Beyond what they should achieve, we've included what they may achieve, including even advanced achievements. An additional checklist is included in each area to let you know how to help your child along the way.

TESTING OBSTACLES

If your child has never taken a test before or has trouble when testing, the Well Planned Start assessments offer a great introduction to testing and are relaxed enough to put any child at ease.

The assessments are not timed, and there are no little circles on separate sheets of paper that children have to navigate. Instead, parents are encouraged to engage children, review instructions, or stop for a break when needed.

In the comfort of your home and with the assurance of a parent administering the assessment, children working through Well Planned Start are able to relax, comprehend, access the information, and enjoy the experience.

Well Planned Start ensures an accurate and enjoyable assessment and placement for children and parents.

#1 START HERE

Begin with the Parent Assessment

PARENT ASSESSMENT

The following pages contain the parent assessment tests for math, language arts, history & geography, science, and Bible. Use this section to begin understanding what your child should know and comprehend. Here are a few tips as you proceed through the questions ahead:

- If you are unsure about the questions and answers, do a quick Internet search.

- If you are unsure whether a topic has been or will be covered, do a little digging. Speak to a representative at your child's previous school or take a quick look through your past or current homeschool curriculum.

- Engage your child in a discussion to see how deep his or her knowledge is. Remembering the significance of an event is more important than knowing a date for a test.

- Try to figure things out together. This is a team effort.

- Lack of information does not necessarily indicate a gap. For example, if you have not covered early American history yet but are sure your child would understand it, give your child credit for abilities.

- Watch your child's general attitude toward learning. If there is a lot of negativity, plan to take a step back to regain a love of learning.

- As you process through this assessment with your child, go with your gut instinct. If you feel your child is good at something, say so. If you feel he or she is struggling, say so.

- Think back to all the times you observed your child doing school work, playing, or having conversations. Do you feel that he or she understands the concepts?

- If you don't feel confident in your knowledge, ask for help from family and friends.

- Ask classmates, former teachers, or other homeschool moms what their observations of your child are.

- Be sure that you administer the entire assessment. If your assessment and your child's performance do not match up, investigate possible causes such as test anxiety or lack of information.

BEYOND ACADEMICS

As you and your child navigate the early elementary years, Well Planned Start provides a great resource for ensuring that you grasp where your child falls academically.

But don't forget that play is still a large part of a 3rd grader's learning environment. Watch for your child to explore a wide variety of interests this year. Incorporate building blocks, sketch pads and other artistic toys, exposure to music, whittling tools, basic sewing kits, and other inexpensive but fun hobby-oriented activities into your child's play. Interests will come and go, and that is okay.

Let this year be a taste-testing opportunity for later development of interests.

NUMBERS TO 999,999

	YES	NO
Can your child read and write numbers up to 999,999?	○	○
Can your child compare numbers up to 999,999?	○	○
Can your child tell you place values up to 999,999?	○	○
Can your child answer: 700,000+___+900 = 750,900	○	○

ADDITION, SUBTRACTION, MULTIPLICATION, AND DIVISION

	YES	NO
Can your child add 4-digit numbers?	○	○
Can your child subtract 4-digit numbers?	○	○
Can your child multiply 3-digit numbers by 1-digit numbers?	○	○
Can your child divide 3-digit numbers by 1-digit numbers?	○	○

$$\begin{array}{r} 425 \\ \times\ \ 4 \\ \hline \end{array}$$

MEASUREMENT

	YES	NO
Can your child convert yards to feet?	○	○
Can your child convert grams to kilograms?	○	○
Can your child convert liters to milliliters?	○	○
Can your child read a thermometer?	○	○

1 yard = 3 feet
1 gram = .001 kilogram
1 liter = 1,000 milliliter

FRACTIONS AND DECIMALS

$$\frac{1}{3} + \frac{1}{5}$$

	YES	NO
Can your child compare fractions?	○	○
Does your child understand equivalent fractions?	○	○
Can your child convert fractions to decimals?	○	○
Can your child convert decimals to fractions?	○	○

MONEY

	YES	NO
Can your child solve story problems involving money?	○	○
Can your child add money?	○	○
Can your child subtract money?	○	○
Can your child make change with as few coins and bills as possible?	○	○

2nd - 4th grade

GETTING EXCITED
MATH

During this stage, math can give lie to the "getting excited" stage of learning, as math facts are anything but exciting. But this is also the perfect stage for using games and fun manipulatives to bring math to life.

Keep your child excited by setting a five minute time limit on those necessary flashcards and using hands-on learning to really drive home the facts.

Language Arts

> A prefix is a group of letters placed *before* the root of a word.
>
> A suffix is a group of letters placed *after* the root of a word.

2nd - 4th grade

GETTING EXCITED

LANGUAGE ARTS

As with math, language arts incorporates the factual component of grammar during this stage. Combine a systematic grammar program with an abundance of reading time to keep learning fun and fresh.

Consider idea and story building to be the important writing concept for this stage, even allowing oral presentations instead of written essays.

READING AND COMPREHENSION

	YES	NO
Is your child able to read chapter books independently?	○	○
Can your child use the dictionary to find words he or she does not understand?	○	○
Is your child able to use the table of contents and index of a book?	○	○
Does your child read on his or her own outside of school hours?	○	○

WRITING

	YES	NO
Can your child write stories, reports, poems, letters, and descriptions?	○	○
Is your child able to find information in an encyclopedia and write a report?	○	○
Does your child understand that paragraphs have topic sentences and supporting details?	○	○
Can your child write a draft, revise it, and proofread it?	○	○

SPELLING AND VOCABULARY

	YES	NO
Does your child spell most words correctly?	○	○
Can your student use a dictionary to check spelling?	○	○
Is your child able to use prefixes, base words, and suffixes?	○	○
Can your child use homophones such as "to," "too," and "two" correctly?	○	○

GRAMMAR AND USAGE

	YES	NO
Does your child know the difference between a complete sentence and a sentence fragment?	○	○
Can your child identify declarative, interrogative, imperative, and exclamatory sentences?	○	○
Can your child tell you what a noun, pronoun, verb, adjective, and adverb is?	○	○
Does your child avoid using double negatives like "I can't never...."?	○	○

LITERATURE

	YES	NO
Can your child tell you what a biography and an autobiography are?	○	○
Does your student know the difference between fiction and nonfiction?	○	○
Does your child enjoy reading poems, stories, and mythology?	○	○
Does your child enjoy reading and going to the library?	○	○

WORLD HISTORY

	YES	NO
Does your child know some stories from Roman history?	○	○
Is your child able to tell you how Rome fell?	○	○
Can your child describe Viking life?	○	○
Does your child know famous Vikings?	○	○

WORLD GEOGRAPHY

	YES	NO
Is your child familiar with geographic terms such as boundary, delta, and strait?	○	○
Can your child use a bar scale on a map to measure distance?	○	○
Does your child know certain locations in Canada?	○	○
Is your child familiar with important rivers around the world?	○	○

UNITED STATES HISTORY

	YES	NO
Can your child name some Native American tribes?	○	○
Does your child know about explorers?	○	○
Is your child able to tell you about the Spanish settlement of North America?	○	○
Can your student tell you about the Thirteen Colonies?	○	○

UNITED STATES GEOGRAPHY

	YES	NO
Does your child know the location of each of the Thirteen Colonies?	○	○
Is your child able to classify the Thirteen colonies as Southern, New England, and Mid-Atlantic.	○	○
Can your child label the different climates of the United States?	○	○
Does your child know where certain natural resources are located in the United States?	○	○

CULTURE

	YES	NO
Is your child able to tell what kind of clothing is worn in different climates?	○	○
Can your child name natural resources from around the world?	○	○
Does your child know what different countries produce?	○	○
Is your child able to tell you the staple foods of different areas of the world?	○	○

Vikings

13 COLONIES

Connecticut
Delaware
Georgia
Maryland
New Jersey
New York
New Hampshire
North Carolina
Pennsylvania
Rhode Island
South Carolina
Massachusetts (included Maine)
Virginia

2nd - 4th grade

GETTING EXCITED

HISTORY & GEOGRAPHY

History continues to be purely fun during these elementary years. Exploration of history through living books, missionary biographies, and religious history is a great way to approach the subject at this stage.

If you haven't already, make sure to work map skills and timelines into your learning during this stage.

9

Science

 Sound is caused by the simple but rapid mechanical vibrations of various elastic bodies.

2nd - 4th grade

GETTING EXCITED

SCIENCE

Science is completely about exploration during this stage. Explore the backyard or park, visit the zoo, check out library books about plants and animals, plant a garden, or find a variety of experiments to enjoy.

Unit studies can be a great option for science at this stage, exploring all you can about scientific subjects of interest to your child.

ANIMAL CLASSIFICATION

	YES	NO
Does your child know the difference between vertebrates and invertebrates?	○	○
Is your child able to determine if an animal is warm-blooded or cold-blooded?	○	○
Can your child tell you the characteristics of each type of animal?	○	○
Does your child know some of the different types of insects?	○	○

HUMAN BODY

	YES	NO
Is your child able to explain the muscular system?	○	○
Can your child explain the skeletal system?	○	○
Does your child know how the eye works?	○	○
Is your child able to tell you how the ear works?	○	○

LIGHT AND OPTICS

	YES	NO
Can your child tell how light travels?	○	○
Is your child able to identify transparent or opaque?	○	○
Does your child know about mirrors and lenses?	○	○
Can your child explain prisms and the visible spectrum?	○	○

SOUND

	YES	NO
Is your child able to tell what causes sound?	○	○
Does your child know how sound travels?	○	○
Can your child describe different qualities of sound like pitch or volume?	○	○
Is your child able to tell you how the human voice works?	○	○

ASTRONOMY

	YES	NO
Does your child know what "universe" means?	○	○
Is your child able to tell you how we explore space?	○	○
Does your child know the names of some stars and constellations?	○	○
Can your child name the planets and some of their moons?	○	○

Planets: Mercury, Venus, Eearth, Mars, Jupiter, Saturn, Uranus, and Neptune

Bible

BIBLE STORIES

	YES	NO
Does your child know the story of King David?	○	○
Can your child tell you the story of Mary and Martha?	○	○
Is your child familiar with the crucifixion story?	○	○
Does your child know the story of Peter and Cornelius?	○	○

Books of the Bible

66 Books

39 Old Testament

27 New Testament

BIBLE REFERENCE TOOLS

	YES	NO
Can your child name all the books of the Bible?	○	○
Is your child familiar with the divisions of the Bible?	○	○
Does your child know how to use cross-references in the Bible?	○	○
Can your child use the footnotes in a study Bible?	○	○

SOVEREIGNTY
God's absolute control and authority over all His creation and creatures.

BIBLE PASSAGES

	YES	NO
Is your child familiar with Proverbs 3:5-6?	○	○
Trust in the Lord with all your heart and lean not on your own understanding...		
Is your child familiar with Psalm 100?	○	○
Shout for joy to the Lord, all the earth. Worship the Lord with gladness...		
Is your child familiar with Psalm 23?	○	○
The Lord is my shepherd, I lack nothing. He makes me lie down in green pastures...		
Is your child familiar with the 10 Commandments?	○	○

THEOLOGY

	YES	NO
Does your child understand that God is sovereign?	○	○
Is your child aware that we must obey God?	○	○
Can your child tell you about heaven and hell?	○	○
Does your child understand love?	○	○

2nd - 4th grade

GETTING EXCITED

BIBLE

These elementary years offer the perfect stage for increasing familiarity with Scripture. Use story Bibles that create connection between the stories of Scripture to help your child see the grand story of redemption.

Consider using Scripture memory songs and a catechism resource to help your child develop a love for hiding God's Word in his heart.

CHURCH HISTORY & MISSIONS

	YES	NO
Does your child know who Martin Luther was?	○	○
Is your child familiar with John Wycliffe?	○	○
Can your child name some reformers?	○	○
Does your child know who William Tyndale was?	○	○

11

MATH

Score	Section
	Numbers to 999,999
	Math Facts
	Measurement
	Fractions & Decimals
	Money

Total Score

Grade Placement

LANGUAGE ARTS

Score	Section
	Reading & Comprehension
	Writing
	Spelling & Vocabulary
	Grammar & Usage
	Literature

Total Score

Grade Placement

HISTORY & GEOGRAPHY

Score	Section
	World History
	World Geography
	United States History
	United States Geography
	Culture

Total Score

Grade Placement

SCIENCE

Score	Section
	Animal Classification
	Human Body
	Light & Optics
	Sound
	Astronomy

Total Score

Grade Placement

BIBLE

Score	Section
	Bible Stories
	Bible Reference Tools
	Bible Passages
	Theology
	Church History and Missions

Total Score

Grade Placement

PARENT ASSESSMENT SCORING

The Well Planned Start was designed to assess a grade level *per subject.* Use the key below to *determine the grade level for each subject.*

1. Count the number of questions you answered yes to in each section. Write the number in the score box to the left of the section.

2. Add the section scores together and place the total in the **Total Score** box.

3. Using the key below, determine the grade assessment for *each subject.*

SUBJECT TEST KEY

- Total Score = 20: Administer the 4th grade test for this subject. Your child may be ready for 5th grade.
- Total Score = 15-19: Your child is ready for the 4th grade.
- Total Score = 10-14: Base your decision on the following **section scores.**
  - Score 2 or less in 1-2 sections: Your child is ready for the 4th grade in this subject, but you can expect to give extra help throughout the year.
  - Score 2 or less in 3-5 sections: Your child should begin this subject at a 3rd grade level.
- All sections = 0-9: Administer the 2nd grade test for this subject. Your child needs additional evaluation.

BIBLE EXCEPTION

Because the development of spiritual growth is not confined to a grade level, the Bible tests for Well Planned Start were designed to cover a range through the following stages of education:

- Starting Out - Preschool - 1st Grade
- Getting Excited: 2nd - 4th Grade
- Beginning to Understand: 5th - 8th Grade
- Learning to Reason: 9th - 12th Grade

When scoring Bible and determining placement, it is recommended to use your discretion in deciding if additional testing is needed or more time studying the topics covered.

WHAT NEXT?

The parent assessment is a guide to what key information your child should know by the end of the 3rd grade. Once you have finished taking the assessment and scoring the results, you can proceed to give the student placement assessment to confirm your results.

PARENT ASSESSMENT NOTES

Use this area to take notes about specific topics, subjects, and processes you feel your child will need help with. After your child has taken the placement test, compare your notes and the scores from the parent assessment to determine subject grades, overall grade level, and plan of action for the coming school year.

DETERMINING A
GRADE LEVEL

Assessment results can indicate grade levels below, at, or above 3rd grade. If you homeschool, you can purchase grade specific curriculum for each subject. However, if you are looking for a means to determine an overall grade level, use the suggestions below in deciding.

- If your child scores above or below a 3rd grade level in math or language arts, you can easily incorporate materials from the assessed grade level. Your child should school in the 4th grade.

- If you child scores below a 3rd grade level in three or more subjects (math, history, science, and language arts), we recommend repeating the 3rd grade.

- If your child scores above a 3rd grade level in three or more subjects (math, history, science, and language arts), we recommend testing with the 4th grade test for advanced placement.

- If your child scores ahead and behind in 2 or more subjects (math, history, science, and language arts), your child should school in the 4th grade.

- Reevaluate every year to be sure that your child is still at the correct grade.

#2 PROCEED

Proceed with Student Placement

STUDENT PLACEMENT TEST

The following pages contain the student placement tests for math, language arts, history and geography, science, and Bible. Along with the instructions on the test, there is also a section beginning on page 39 to reference as you watch your child work through the questions and answers. Utilizing this student placement test administrator guide will allow you to recognize the areas of struggle for your child and the point where problem solving breaks down.

The assessments ahead are a tool for you to use to better understand your child's academic needs. Here are a few more tips to use when administering these evaluations:

- Choose a calm day and a quiet space for assessment.

- Make sure your child is fresh and feeling well. Do not administer the assessments after three hours of calculus.

- Choose a time that is calm and fresh for you as well, as you will be working through the assessment with your child. It is important to minimize distractions for both you and your child during this time.

- Unless you have a child who enjoys tests and challenges, present these assessments as a new kind of activity or worksheet. If you say "test," they may lock up.

- Each assessment is printed on perforated pages. Simply remove each page and give it to the child to work on.

- Make sure your child understands the directions well.

- If the instructions are written in terms your child does not understand, feel free to change the wording.

- Take your time! These are not timed assessments. You are looking for correct thinking, not speed.

- As you process through this assessment with your child, go with your gut instinct. If you feel your child is good at something, say so. If you feel he or she is struggling, say so.

- Lack of information does not necessarily indicate a gap. For example, if you have not covered early American history yet but are sure your child would understand it, give your child credit for abilities.

- Look for creative thought processes. If you think an answer is weird, ask your child to explain how he or she arrived at it. If the logic behind the answer makes sense, give your child some credit.

- For concrete questions like math or science, watch for correct processes. Your child may be solving everything correctly and just writing down a wrong number or making a mistake in computation. If you are unsure, provide a new, similar problem for your child to work, or ask him to take another look. Having your child show his work will help.

- If you feel that there is a significant gap or that your child has not "gotten" the information after repeated exposure, please seek a professional evaluation for underlying issues. Whether you assign a label or not, understanding your child will make you a better teacher.

1. Is 127,201 greater than or less than 600,000?

2. 951,600 is 10,000 more than what?

3. Which number is in the ten thousands place in 612,720?

4. 700,000 + _____ + 900 = 750,900

5.
$$3924 + 4186$$

6.
$$8054 - 3225$$

7.
$$773 \times 7$$

8. $100 \div 3 =$

9. 11 ft. = _____ yds _____ ft

10. 2928 g = _____ kg _____ g

11. 5 L 15 mL = _____ mL

Math

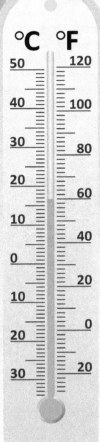

°C   °F
50   120
40   100
30   80
20   60
10   40
 0   20
10   0
20   20
30   20

12. What is the temperature in Fahrenheit?

13. Circle which is larger:

$$\frac{3}{5} \qquad \frac{5}{9}$$

14. Fill in the missing numbers

$$\frac{1}{3} = \frac{2}{\boxed{}} = \frac{\boxed{}}{12}$$

15. Write the mixed number as a decimal.

$$4\frac{37}{100} = \boxed{}$$

16   USE A SEPARATE SHEET OF PAPER TO WORK YOUR MATH PROBLEMS

16. Write 12.72 as a fraction.

17. The budget is $5,000 per month. If the house payment is $1,275 and the electricity is $322, how much money is available for other bills?

18. $25.69 + $15.66 =

19. $50.04 - $22.50 =

20. Circle the bills and coins needed to make change.

$40.00 - $31.22 =

Read this selection and answer the questions.

A musical instrument is a device created to make musical sounds. Anything that makes a sound can be used as a musical instrument. The history of musical instruments goes back to the beginning of culture. People first used instruments for rituals: a hunter might use a trumpet to signal a successful hunt; a drum might be used in a religious ceremony.

Cultures later composed and performed a set of sounds called a melody for entertainment. Musical instruments were needed. Some historians report that the earliest musical instrument was a simple flute. Many of the earliest musical instruments were made from animal skins, bone, wood, and other non-durable materials.

Musical instruments were developed separately in the different countries and regions of the world, but when civilizations shared information amongst themselves, the development of instruments spread. For example, cultures of North America, South America, and Central America used similar instruments and shared these ideas of making instruments that were alike in some way.

a. Who might use musical instruments?

b. What is a musical instrument?

c. When were musical instruments first used?

d. Why were musical melodies composed?

e. How were musical instruments used?

2. Circle the definition for the word that comes between seam and sewing.

schedule - a plan of when certain actions or events will be carried out.

sensitive - able to smell, hear, taste, feel, or see very well.

signal - a movement, action, or device used to give directions, warning, or other information.

solution - the act or process of solving a problem or question.

Language Arts

3. If you wanted to find a particular page that contains a specific piece of information in a book, would you use the table of contents or the index?

4. **Read this selection and circle how much you enjoyed it.**

Maria Mitchell was born in 1818 in Massachusetts. She was raised as a Quaker. The Quaker religion values education equally for boys and girls. So although many other young girls could not attend school at this time, the Quaker families sent their daughters to school.

In fact, Maria's father was her first principal. When Maria was 11, her father built his own school, and she was a student in this school. Maria also served as a teaching assistant. A teaching assistant is someone who is a teacher's helper.

Because Maria showed an early interest in the stars, Mr. Mitchell taught Maria about the telescope and astronomy. Astronomy is the study of the universe beyond the earth which includes stars, planets, comets, and galaxies.

5. Circle the correct expression in each row.

☐ letter   ☐ story   ☐ description

☐ poem   ☐ report

1. an account of imaginary or real people and events told for entertainment
2. an account given of a particular matter, especially in the form of an official document
3. a piece of writing that partakes of the nature of both speech and song that is nearly always rhythmical, usually metaphorical, and often exhibits such formal elements as meter, rhyme, and stanzaic structure
4. a written, typed, or printed communication, especially one sent in an envelope by mail or messenger
5. a spoken or written representation or account of a person, object, or event

6. Circle the sources you would use to write a report.

encyclopedia

fiction book

nonfiction book

any website

library database

Language Arts

7.

Underline the topic sentence in this paragraph.

Milton Hershey is remembered as someone who built an entire city and helped people get jobs. He is remembered for someone who made a school for children who did not have families. He is someone who made a medical center to help those who are sick and someone who made that yummy chocolate that most of us throughout the world enjoy.

8.

Match each stage of writing with what you do.

[ ] revise

[ ] proofread

[ ] draft

1. make a preliminary version of a piece of writing

2. make corrections and rewrite

3. read and mark errors

9.

Look at the pictures and circle the correct spelling.

puddel   puddle   caterpillar   catapiller   toorkey   turkey

10.

This word is misspelled. Use the dictionary page to the right to correct the spelling.

lemin

correct spelling:

leisure - freedom from work or other duties that take time and effort; free time.

lemon - a small citrus fruit with yellow skin and sour juice.

lens - a piece of clear material such as glass that bends light rays passing through it.

leopard - a large mammal with short yellow or gray fur and black spots.

11. Circle the prefix, underline the base word, and box the suffix in this word.

unsafely

12. Select the correct words to finish the sentences.

- [ ] two
- [ ] to
- [ ] too

1. Would you like to come _____?

2. I would like _____ milkshakes, please.

3. Can we get _____ the ice cream parlor?

13. Match the type of sentence and the example.

- [ ] imperative
- [ ] interrogative
- [ ] exclamatory
- [ ] declarative

1. The rain caused the temperature to drop.

2. Have you heard the news about the new shopping mall?

3. Please take this bill to the counter across the hall.

4. You won!

14. Identify these as
S - complete sentences
F - fragments

- [ ] Because of the storm.

- [ ] I like to go to the beach and play in the sand.

- [ ] After the boys finish hockey practice.

- [ ] Since we only have two vehicles, would you like to ride with me?

15. Match the part of speech with its definition.

- [ ] adjective
- [ ] verb
- [ ] noun
- [ ] pronoun
- [ ] adverb

1. person, place, thing, or idea

2. refers to a noun

3. describes a noun or pronoun

4. describes a verb, adjective, or other adverb

5. shows action or a state of being

Language Arts

16.

This sentence has a double negative.

Cross out one of the words to make it correct.

I can't never seem to get the temperature of the burner just right.

17. What is the difference between a biography and an autobiography?

a. A biography is written by the person and an autobiography is written by someone else.

b. A biography is written by someone else and an autobiography is written by the person.

c. There is no difference.

18. What is the difference between fiction and nonfiction?

a. Fiction is made-up and nonfiction is true.

b. Fiction is true and nonfiction is made up.

c. There is no difference.

19. Match the literary type with the example.

- [ ] myth
- [ ] poem
- [ ] story

1. My Shadow
2. The Lion, the Witch, and the Wardrobe
3. The Iliad

20. Circle the things you would find in a library.

books

animals

DVDs

things to buy

computers

a bounce house

magazines

newspapers

1. Romulus and Remus were:

☐
- a. twins raised by a wolf
- b. the founders of Rome
- c. both a and b

2. Circle the empires that conquered the Roman empire:

Franks

Aborigine

Burgundians

Wadani

Visigoths

Musai

Vandals

Aztec

Goths

3. Circle the objects associated with Vikings.

longboats

phalanx

swords

gladiolus

Thor's hammer

papyrus

4. Match the Viking with what he or she did.

☐ Ivar the Boneless

☐ Erik the Red   ☐ Rollo the Viking

☐ Bjorn Ironside   ☐ Leif Erikson

1. legendary king of Sweden who lived sometime in the 9th century

2. Norwegian Viking, remembered in medieval and Icelandic saga sources as having founded the first Norse settlement in Greenland

3. an Icelandic explorer and the first known European to have discovered North America (excluding Greenland), before Christopher Columbus

4. Viking leader and commander who invaded what is now England

5. a Viking who became the first ruler of Normandy, a region of France

Match the geographic term with the definition.

5.
1. a line that marks the limits of an area; a dividing line

2. a landform that forms from deposition of sediment carried by a river as the flow leaves its mouth and enters slower-moving or standing water

3. a naturally formed, narrow, typically navigable waterway that connects two larger bodies of water

☐ delta

☐ strait

☐ boundary

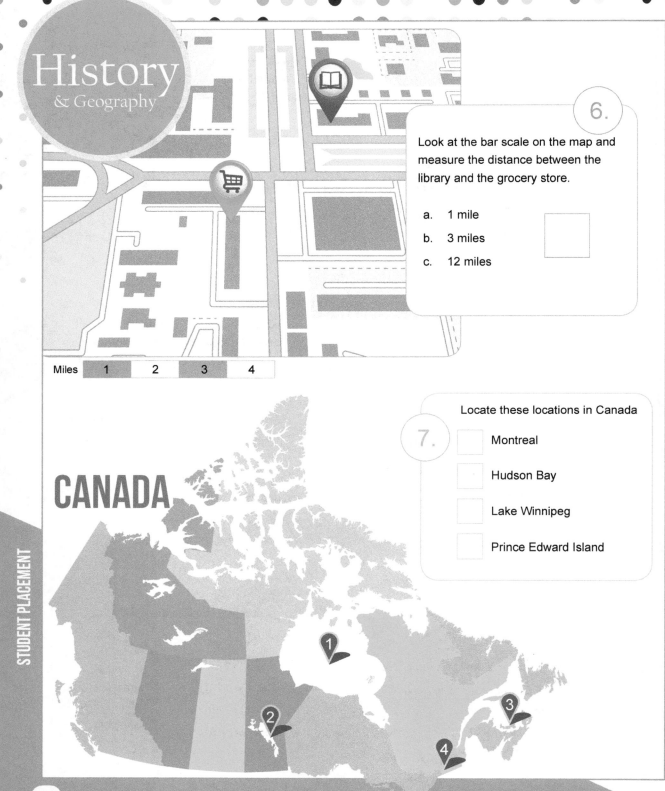

6.

Look at the bar scale on the map and measure the distance between the library and the grocery store.

a. 1 mile

b. 3 miles

c. 12 miles

Miles | 1 | 2 | 3 | 4

CANADA

Locate these locations in Canada

7.

Montreal

Hudson Bay

Lake Winnipeg

Prince Edward Island

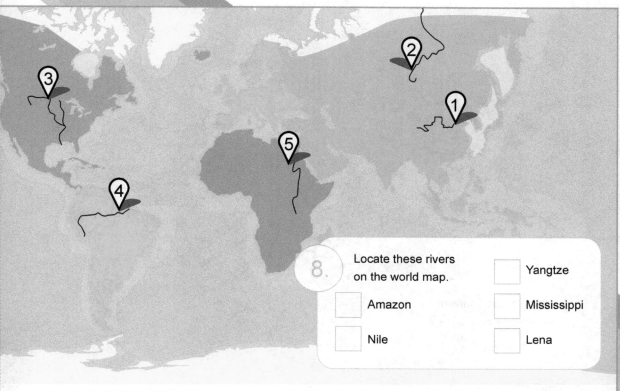

8. Locate these rivers on the world map.

- [ ] Amazon
- [ ] Nile
- [ ] Yangtze
- [ ] Mississippi
- [ ] Lena

9. Circle the names of Native American tribes found in the U.S.

Cherokee

Aztec

Pawnee

Quechua

Shoshone

10. Match the explorer with what he discovered.

- [ ] Hernando de Soto
- [ ] Henry Hudson
- [ ] John Cabot
- [ ] Francisco Vasquez de Coronado

1. made two attempts on behalf of English merchants to find a prospective Northwest Passage to Cathay (today's China) via a route above the Arctic Circle
2. led a large expedition from Mexico to present-day Kansas through parts of the southwestern United States between 1540 and 1542
3. the first documented European to have crossed the Mississippi River
4. discovered the coast of North America under the commission of Henry VII of England

25

11. Locate these Spanish settlements on the map.

☐ St. Augustine

☐ Santa Fe

☐ San Diego

12. Label each colony.
R = royal
P = proprietary
C = charter

☐ Connecticut

☐ Delaware

☐ Georgia

☐ Maryland

☐ Massachusetts

☐ New Hampshire

☐ New Jersey

☐ New York

☐ North Carolina

☐ Pennsylvania

☐ Rhode Island

☐ South Carolina

☐ Virginia

13. Label each colony.
S = Southern
M = Mid-Atlantic
N = New England

☐ Connecticut

☐ Delaware

☐ Georgia

☐ Maryland

☐ Massachusetts

☐ New Hampshire

☐ New Jersey

☐ New York

☐ North Carolina

☐ Pennsylvania

☐ Rhode Island

☐ South Carolina

☐ Virginia

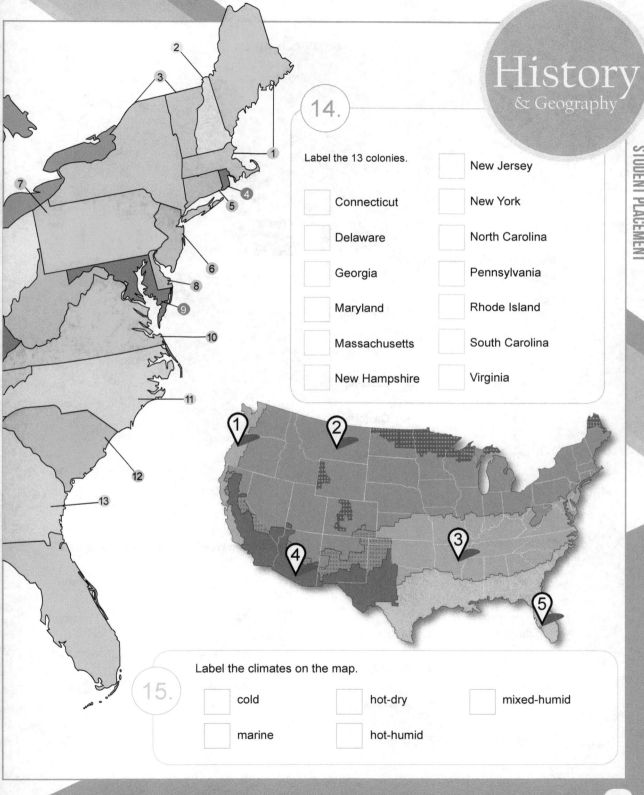

14.

Label the 13 colonies.

☐ Connecticut	☐ New Jersey
☐ Delaware	☐ New York
☐ Georgia	☐ North Carolina
☐ Maryland	☐ Pennsylvania
☐ Massachusetts	☐ Rhode Island
☐ New Hampshire	☐ South Carolina
	☐ Virginia

15.

Label the climates on the map.

☐ cold   ☐ hot-dry   ☐ mixed-humid

☐ marine   ☐ hot-humid

16. Match the natural resource with where it is found.

☐	oil	1. Wyoming
☐	lumber	2. Texas
☐	fishing	3. Louisiana
☐	coal	4. California
☐	agriculture	5. Alaska

17. Match the natural resource with the country it is found.

☐	oil	1. China
☐	lumber	2. Indonesia
☐	fishing	3. Saudi Arabia
☐	coal	4. Australia
☐	agriculture	5. USA

18. Match the type of clothing with the climate.

☐	sari	1. desert
☐	fur-lined parka	2. savannah
☐	African tunic	3. tropical
☐	Aborigine loin cloth	4. polar

19. Match the product with the country that produces it.

	jewelry		1.	China
	vehicles		2.	India
	machines		3.	United States
	personal computers		4.	Japan
	transportation equipment		5.	Germany

20. Match the main food with the correct country.

	corn		1.	India
	rice		2.	United States
	wheat		3.	Germany
	potatoes		4.	China
	beets		5.	Netherlands

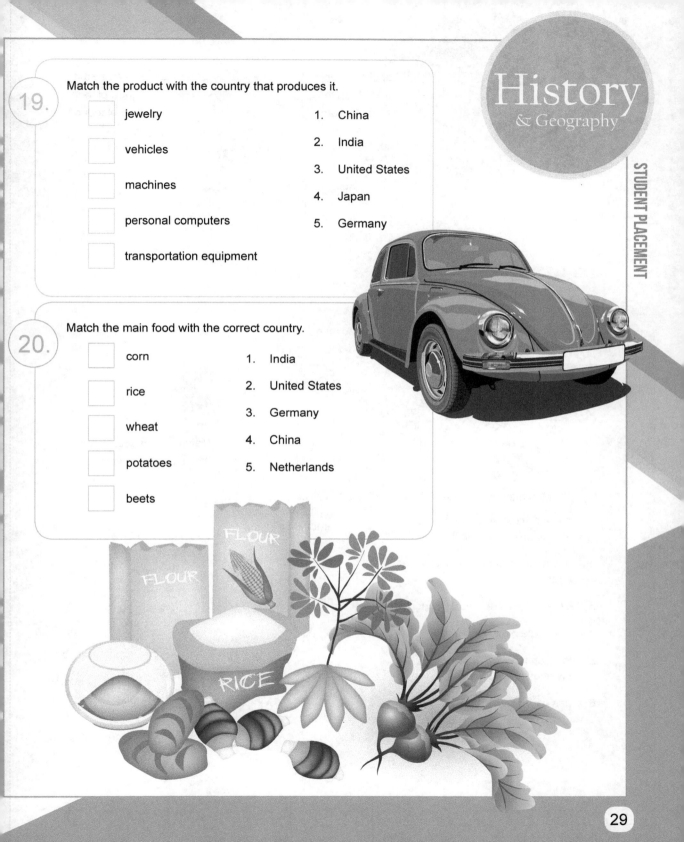

Science

1.

Label each animal
V - Vertebrate
I - Invertebrate

☐ cat

☐ chicken

☐ spider

☐ clam

☐ ladybug

2.

Label each animal
W - Warm-blooded
C - Cold-blooded

☐ frog

☐ snake

☐ sheep

☐ shark

☐ parrot

3.

Match the type of animal with its characteristics.

1. has fur; most give birth to live young; produces milk

2. has feathers and wings; lays eggs

3. lives in the water; most lay eggs

4. has scales; most lay eggs

5. lives on land and in water; most lay eggs

6. has an external skeleton and jointed legs

☐ amphibian

☐ fish

☐ mammal

☐ insect

☐ bird

☐ reptile

4.

Match each insect with another that is closely related to it.

☐ assassin bug

☐ Goliath beetle

☐ house fly

☐ grasshopper

☐ moth

1. ladybug
2. butterfly
3. cricket
4. stink bug
5. bee

5. Match the type of muscle with its definition.

◻ involuntary muscle

◻ cardiac muscle

◻ voluntary muscle

◻ skeletal muscle

1. action is normally controlled by an individual's will

2. a muscle that contracts without conscious control

3. a muscle that is connected to the skeleton to form part of the mechanical system that moves the limbs and other parts of the body

4. the muscular tissue of the heart

6. Label the bones of the body.

◻ femur / thigh bone

◻ humerus / arm bone

◻ ribs

◻ pelvis / hip

◻ sternum / breastbone

7. Match each part of the eye with what it does.

◻ optic nerve

◻ cornea

◻ pupil

◻ retina

◻ lens

1. protects the eye

2. allows light into the eye

3. focuses light

4. receives the focused light

5. transfers an image to the brain

Science

8. Match each part of the ear with what it does.

1. collects sound from the environment
2. carries sound waves into the ear
3. transfers sound waves
4. carries the sound to the brain

☐ ear drum

☐ auditory nerve

☐ outer ear

☐ ear canal

9. Label each object
T - transparent
O - opaque

☐ clear glass

☐ water

☐ aluminum foil

☐ wood

10. Light travels by

☐

a. electromagnetic waves

b. making bursts

c. breaking the sound barrier

11. Match the mirrors and lenses with their type.

☐ concave mirror   ☐ convex mirror   ☐ concave lens   ☐ convex lens

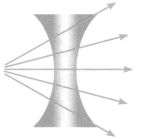

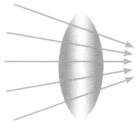

A   B   C   D

12.

Label the six colors of the visible spectrum.

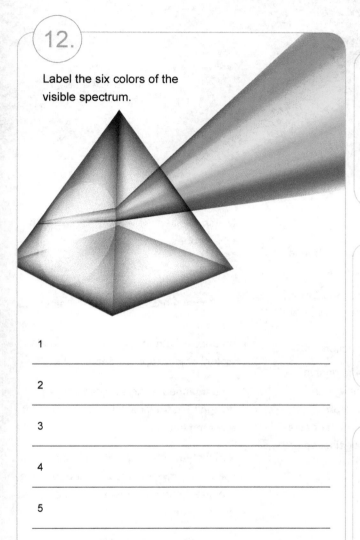

1

_____

2

_____

3

_____

4

_____

5

_____

6

_____

13.

Sound is caused by

a. the visible spectrum

b. packets of energy

c. vibrations

14.

Sound travels by waves through

a. solids

b. liquids

c. gases

d. all of the above

15.

Pitch is determined by; volume is determined by:

a. height of waves; speed of waves

b. speed of waves; height of waves

c. number of waves; length of waves

Explain to your test administrator how the human voice is produced.

16.

17.

Number the planets in order from the sun outward.

☐ Saturn

☐ Earth

☐ Neptune

1 Mercury

☐ Venus

☐ Uranus

☐ Mars

5 Jupiter

18.

☐

Universe means

a. all existing matter and space considered as a whole.

b. a system of millions or billions of stars, together with gas and dust, held together by gravitational attraction.

c. a cloud of gas and dust in outer space, visible in the night sky either as an indistinct bright patch or as a dark silhouette against other luminous matter.

19.

Match each space exploration tool with what it does.

☐ space shuttle   ☐ satellite

☐ space probe   ☐ telescope

1. an optical instrument designed to make distant objects appear nearer

2. an unmanned exploratory spacecraft designed to transmit information about its environment

3. a rocket-launched spacecraft, able to land like an unpowered aircraft, used to make repeated journeys between the earth and earth's orbit

4. an artificial body placed in orbit around the earth or moon or another planet in order to collect information or for communication

20.

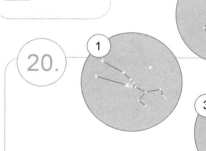

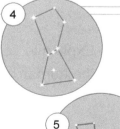

Match the constellation with its name.

☐ the Big Dipper

☐ the Little Dipper

☐ Orion

☐ Taurus

☐ Gemini

34

Bible

1. Circle the events of King David's life.

becomes friends with Jonathan

hides the spies under the straw roof

asks help for watering his camels

plays the harp for King Saul

uses a slingshot to defeat Goliath

marries Ruth

becomes king of Israel

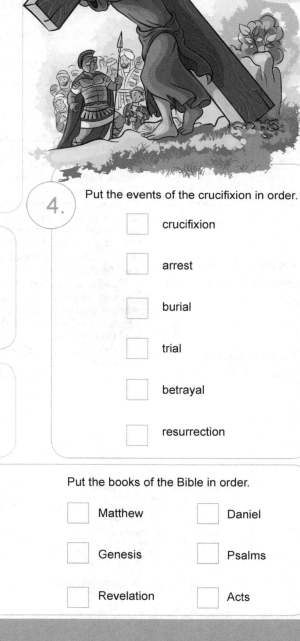

2. Mary and Martha were

a. helpers in the temple

b. Jesus' friends

c. Moses' sisters

3. Explain what Peter and Cornelius did.

4. Put the events of the crucifixion in order.

☐ crucifixion

☐ arrest

☐ burial

☐ trial

☐ betrayal

☐ resurrection

5. Put the books of the Bible in order.

☐ Matthew   ☐ Daniel

☐ Genesis   ☐ Psalms

☐ Revelation   ☐ Acts

35

Bible

6. Match the Bible book with its description.

1. tells about the nation of Israel

2. tells how Israel took the promised land

3. gives wisdom for life

4. tells the story of Jesus

5. is a letter written by Paul

☐ Joshua

☐ Luke

☐ Romans

☐ Proverbs

☐ Exodus

51

18 *j* Jer. 31:35
21 *m* Ps. 104:25, 26
22 *n* ch. 8:17; 9:1
26 *o* ch. 3:22; 11:7; Isa. 6:8
p ch. 5:1; 9:6; 1 Cor. 11:7;
Eph. 4:24; Col. 3:10;
James 3:9 *q* ch. 9:2; Ps.
8:6-8; James 3:7
27 *r* ch. 2:18, 21-23; 5:2;
Mal. 2:15; Matt. 19:4;
Mark 10:6
28 *s* ch. 9:1, 7

light to rule the night—and the stars. **17** And God set them in the expanse of the heavens to give light on the earth, **18** to *j*rule over the day and over the night, and to separate the light from the darkness. And God saw that it was good. **19** And there was evening and there was morning, the fourth day.

20 And God said, "Let the waters swarm with swarms of living creatures, and let birds[1] fly above the earth across the expanse of the heavens." **21** So *m*God created the great sea creatures and every living creature that moves, with which the waters swarm, according to their kinds, and every winged bird according to its kind. And God saw that it was good. **22** And God blessed them, saying, *n*"Be fruitful and multiply and fill the waters in the seas, and let birds multiply on the earth." **23** And there was evening and there was morning, the fifth day.

24 And God said, "Let the earth bring forth living creatures according to their kinds—livestock and creeping things and beasts of the earth according to their kinds." And it was so. **25** And God made the beasts of the earth according to their kinds and the livestock according to their kinds, and everything that creeps on the ground according to its kind. And God saw that it was good.

26 Then God said, *o*"Let us make man[2] in our image, *p*after our likeness. And *q*let them have dominion over the fish of the sea and over the birds of the heavens and over the livestock and over all the earth and over every creeping thing that creeps on the earth."

27   So God created man in his own image,
          in the image of God he created him;
          *r*male and female he created them.

28 And God blessed them. And God said to them, *s*"Be fruitful and multiply and fill the

[1] Or *flying things*; see Leviticus 11:19-20 [2] The Hebrew word for *man (adam)* is the generic term for mankind and becomes the proper name *Adam*

7. In the Bible page draw a box around the cross reference verses.

8. In the Bible page draw a circle around the footnote area.

Isa. 40:25–26) is mentioned here only in a brief phrase, almost as if it were an afterthought. The focus of Genesis 1 is on the earth; the focus of the rest of the Bible is on man (male and female) as the pinnacle of God's creation and the object of his great salvation.

1:20–23 Having previously described the creation of the **waters** and the **expanse of the heavens**, this section focuses on how they are filled with appropriate creatures of different kinds. As reproductive organisms, they are blessed by God so that they may be fruitful and fill their respective regions.

man is not made in the image of angels, nor is there any indication that angels participated in the creation of human beings. Many Christians and some Jews have taken "us" to be God speaking to himself, since God alone does the making in Gen. 1:27 (cf. 5:1); this would be the first hint of the Trinity in the Bible (cf. 1:2).

1:27 There has been debate about the expression **image of God**. Many scholars point out the idea, commonly used in the ancient Near East, of the king who was the visible representative of the deity; thus the king ruled on behalf of the god. Since v. 26 links the image of God with the exercise of

9. Fill in the blanks for Proverbs 3:5-6.

Trust in the _____ with all your _____ and lean

not on your own _____; in all your _____

submit to him, and he will make your paths _____.

10. Fill in the blanks for Psalm 100:1-2.

Shout for _____ to the Lord, all the _____. Worship the

_____ with gladness; come before him with _____ _____.

11. Fill in the blanks for Ps. 23.

The Lord is my _____, I lack

_____. He makes me _____

down in green pastures, he leads me

beside quiet _____, he

_____ my soul. He guides

me along the _____ paths

for his name's sake.

12. Fill in the blanks for the 10 Commandments. (from Ex. 20:3-17)

1. You shall have no other _____ before _____.

2. You shall not _____ for yourself an _____.

3. You shall not _____ the _____ of the Lord your God.

4. Remember the _____ day.

5. Honor your _____ and your _____.

6. You shall not _____.

7. You shall not commit _____.

8. You shall not _____.

9. You shall not give _____ testimony.

10. You shall not _____.

13. Sovereign means

a. lower in rank or position

b. knowing everything

c. possessing supreme or ultimate power

37

Bible

14. Circle the ways you can obey God.

obeying mom and dad　　being silly in class

throwing a fit　　being kind to others

obeying teachers　　making fun of others

15. True or False: _____

Heaven and hell are real places.

16. How do you show love?

17. Martin Luther ☐

a. began the Reformation by posting his Ninety-five Theses, which attacked the church for allowing the sale of indulgences.

b. became the Grand Commissioner for indulgences in Germany.

c. was the pope who helped provoke the Reformation in the sixteenth century.

18. John Wycliffe is known for ☐

a. preaching about the absolute authority of the Bible

b. translating the Bible into the common language

c. inventing the moveable-type printing press

19. Circle the names of some reformers.

Johannes Hus

John Tetzel

John Calvin

Thomas More

Peter Waldo

20. William Tyndale is known for ☐

a. destroying secular art and culture

b. making himself head of the Christian Church in England

c. translating the Bible into English

STUDENT PLACEMENT TEST ADMINISTRATOR GUIDE

In the following pages, you will find the student placement test administrator guide. This section walks you through assessing your child during the test and includes an answer key and scoring chart.

SECTIONS

Each subject test is divided into 5 sections. This allows you to break up the test as needed and evaluate based on both individual section scores and an overall subject score.

ASSESS

This column includes questions and information to help you understand the goal of the test question. Use these questions to help identify and assess knowledge of the subject matter or understanding of processes, whether or not your child answers correctly.

ANSWERS

This column indicates the correct answer for the questions. Occasionally this column is merged with the notes column to give ample room for detailed answer information.

NOTES

In order to help you understand how a child should arrive at an answer, we have included this section to give the details of the processes. As well, this area includes helpful tips on the goals for the question and how your child should arrive at answers.

SCORES

Use this area to indicate a correct answer or sufficient knowledge to give credit for the question. Use either a checkmark or a number one. As your child completes each section, add up the marks and place the total in the "Section Score" box at the top of the section. These scores will be used to tally your child's subject and overall scores at the end of the test.

SUMMARY

The final page of this section is used to summarize the section scores, subject scores, and overall grade placement.

TEST HACKS

Combat test nervousness and reduce stress by utilizing some of these Test Hacks.

1. Prepare snacks in advance, including protein to munch on during the test and other snacks for break time.

2. When choosing a test location, consider where your child learns best, even if that means lounging in a hammock or sitting on an exercise ball.

3. Grab a stress ball, Silly Putty, gum, or other little tools to have on hand to combat fidgetiness.

4. If your child seems nervous, add in a little fun by periodically surprising them with a question like, "What is your favorite color?" or asking them to do something funny like draw a goofy alien with horns.

5. If you begin seeing signs of stress during the test, take a break to do jumping jacks, take 10 deep breaths, or go for a 15-minute walk or bike ride.

6. Diffusing a citrus oil like lemon, grapefruit, or orange is good to alleviate stress and improve focus without using overly calming scents like lavender.

PLACEMENT TEST GUIDE

Use when administering and scoring

STUDENT PLACEMENT TEST GUIDE

#	Assess	Answer	Notes	✔
NUMBERS TO 999,999			Section Score	
1	Does your child understand the concepts of greater than and less than?	Less than.	Compare the hundred thousands place. 1 is less than 6.	
2	Does your child understand how to add multiples of ten?	941,600	951,600-10,000=941,600	
3	Does child understand that changing a digit's position changes the value of the number?	1		
4	Is your child able to write numbers in expanded form.	50,000	This is known as expanded form.	
ADDITION, SUBTRACTION, MULTIPLICATION, AND DIVISION			Section Score	
5	Does your child keep the columns lined up and carry the numbers properly?	8,110	Be sure that your student lines up the columns, adds, and carries the numbers correctly.	
6	Does your child keep the columns lined up and borrow numbers properly?	4,829	Be sure that your student lines up the columns, borrows numbers, and subtracts correctly.	
7	Does your child multiply each digit individually and carry the numbers correctly?	5,411	Be sure you child multiplies, carries numbers, shifts places, and adds columns correctly.	
8	Does your child write the numbers in the proper places and bring down numbers correctly?	33.33..., 33 r. 1, or 33 1/3 are all acceptable answers. Be sure your student divides, multiplies, subtracts, and brings down numbers correctly.		
MEASUREMENT			Section Score	
9	Does your child know how many feet are in a yard?	3 yds 2 ft	There are three feet in one yard. 3 yds = 9 ft. There are 2 ft left over.	
10	Does your child know how many grams are in a kilogram?	2 kg 928 g	There are 1,000 g in 1 kg. 2 kg = 2,000 g. There are 928 g leftover.	
11	Does your child know how many milliliters are in a liter?	5,015 mL	There are 1,000 mL in 1 L. 5 L = 5,000 mL. Add in 15 mL.	
12	Does your child understand that thermometers measure temperature?	60° F		

STUDENT PLACEMENT TEST GUIDE

#	Assess	Answer	Notes	✔
FRACTIONS AND DECIMALS			Section Score	
13	Does your child know to find the common denominator before comparing fractions?	3/5	Find the lowest common denominator: 45. 3/5 = 27/45 5/9 = 25/45	
14	Does your child understand that the same portion can be written as different fractions?	1/3 = 2/6 = 4/12	Find equivalent fractions by multiplying the numerator and denominator by the same numbers.	
15	Does your child know the process for converting fractions to decimals?	4.37		
16	Does your child know the process for converting decimals to fractions?	12 18/25	12.72 = 12 72/100 Reduce 72/100 by dividing the numerator and denomiatior by 4: 18/25. (Note: If the fraction is not reduced, give credit for 72/100, but discuss the importance of a habit of reducing fractions.)	
MONEY			Section Score	
17	Does your child understand the basics of making a budget?	$3,403.00	$5,000-$1275=$3725. $3725-$322=$3403.	
18	Does your child line up the columns and carry the numbers correctly?	$41.35	Be sure your student lines up the decimals and columns, adds, and carries the numbers correctly.	
19	Does your child line up the columns and borrow the numbers correctly?	$27.54	Be sure your student lines up the decimals and columns, borrows, and subtracts correctly.	
20	Does your child understand how to make change?	$8.78	Best option:1 $5 bill, 3 $1 bills, 3 quarters, 3 pennies	

STUDENT PLACEMENT TEST GUIDE

#	Assess	Answer	✔
READING AND COMPREHENSION		Section Score	
1	Is your child able to understand and remember what he or she reads? Does he or she go back to a text to find the answer to a question?	Who might use musical instruments? a hunter, a religious leader What is a musical instrument? a device created to make musical sounds When were musical instruments first used? at the beginning of culture Why were musical melodies composed? for entertainment How were musical instruments used? to signal hunts, for religious ceremonies, for entertainment	
2	Does your child know how to find a definition in a dictionary?	sensitive - able to smell, hear, taste, feel, or see very well	
3	Does your child know what a table of contents and index are?	index	
4	Does your child enjoy reading? If not, was the piece boring or is reading a struggle?	There is no right or wrong answer to this question. It is for you to learn your student's general attitude toward reading.	
WRITING		Section Score	
5	Does your child know what stories, reports, poems, letters, and descriptions are?	letter: 4 poem: 3 story: 1 report: 2 description: 5	
6	Is your child familiar with research resources?	encyclopedia nonfiction book library database	
7	Does your child understand that a paragraph has a topic sentence?	Milton Hershey is remembered as someone who built an entire city and helped people get jobs.	
8	Does your child understand the stages of writing?	revise: 2 proofread: 3 draft: 1	
SPELLING AND VOCABULARY		Section Score	
9	Is your child able to recognize misspelled words?	puddle caterpillar turkey	
10	Does your child know how to correct a misspelled word?	lemon	

#	Assess	Answer	Notes	✔
11	Does your child know what a prefix, suffix, and base word are?	Prefix: un-, base word: safe, suffix: -ly		
12	Does your child understand what homophones are?	two: 2 to: 3 too: 1		

GRAMMAR AND USAGE | | | Section Score | |

#	Assess	Answer	Notes	✔
13	Does your child know what declarative, interrogative, exclamatory, and imperative sentences are?	imperative - 3 interrogative - 2 exclamatory - 4 declarative - 1		
14	Does your child understand what a complete sentence is?	F - Because of the storm. S - I like to go to the beach and play in the sand. F - After the boys finish hockey practice. S - Since we only have two vehicles, would you like to ride with me?		
15	Does you child know what nouns, pronouns, adjectives, adverbs, and verbs are?	adjective: 3 verb: 5 noun: 1 pronoun: 2 adverb: 4		
16	Does your child understand what a double negative is?	I can never seem to get the temperature of the burner just right. I can't seem to get the temperature of the burner just right.		

LITERATURE | | | Section Score | |

#	Assess	Answer	Notes	✔
17	Does your child know what biographies and autobiographies are?	b		
18	Does your child know what fiction and nonfiction are?	a		
19	Is your child familiar with poems, stories, and myths?	myth: 3 poem: 1 story: 2		
20	Is your child familiar with your library?	books DVDs computers magazines newspapers If your student has attended special events at the library, he or she may have seen some other things on the list. But these are not there on a regular basis.		

STUDENT PLACEMENT TEST GUIDE

#	Assess	Answer	Notes	✓
WORLD HISTORY			Section Score	
1	Is your child familiar with the story of how Rome was founded?	c		
2	Does your child know how the Roman Empire fell?	Franks Burgundians Visigoths Vandals Goths		
3	Is your child familiar with Viking life?	longboats swords Thor's hammer		
4	Does your child know some famous Vikings?	Ivar the Boneless - 4 Erik the Red - 2 Bjorn Ironside - 1 Rollo the Viking - 5 Leif Erikson - 3		
WORLD GEOGRAPHY			Section Score	
5	Is your child familiar with geographic terms like boundary, delta, and strait?	delta - 2 strait - 3 boundary - 1		
6	Does your child know what a bar scale on a map is?	b		
7	Is your child familiar with the geography of Canada?	Montreal - 4 Hudson Bay - 1 Lake Winnipeg - 2 Prince Edward Island - 3		
8	Does your child know some of the major rivers of the world?	Amazon: 4 Nile: 5 Yangtze: 1 Mississippi: 3 Lena: 2		
UNITED STATES HISTORY			Section Score	
9	Is your child familiar with Native American culture?	Cherokee Pawnee Shoshone		
10	Does your child know some famous explorers?	Hernando de Soto - 3 Henry Hudson - 1 John Cabot - 4 Francisco Vasquez de Coronado - 2		
11	Is your child familiar with English, Spanish, French, and Dutch settlements of the New World?	St. Augustine - 3 Santa Fe - 2 San Diego - 1		

STUDENT PLACEMENT TEST GUIDE

#	Assess	Answer	Notes	✔
12	Does your child understand that each colony was founded for a different reason?	Connecticut - C Delaware - P Georgia - R Maryland - P Massachusetts - C	New Hampshire - R Pennsylvania - P New Jersey - R Rhode Island - C New York - R South Carolina - R North Carolina - R Virginia - R	
UNITED STATES GEOGRAPHY			Section Score	
13	Is your child familiar with the Southern, Mid-Atlantic, and New England colonies?	Connecticut - N Delaware - M Georgia - S Maryland - S Massachusetts - N New Hampshire - N	New Jersey - M New York - M North Carolina - S Pennsylvania - M Rhode Island - N South Carolina - S Virginia - S	
14	Does your child know some of the colonies?	Connecticut - 5 Delaware - 8 Georgia - 13 Maryland - 9 Massachusetts - 1	New Hampshire - 2 Rhode Island - 4 New Jersey - 6 South Carolina - 12 New York - 3 Virginia - 10 North Carolina - 11 Pennsylvania - 7	
15	Does your child understand that different parts of the U.S. have their own climates?	cold: 2 marine: 1 hot-dry: 4 hot-humid: 5 mixed-humid: 3		
16	Does your child understand that each part of the U.S. offers a different natural resource?	oil - 2 lumber - 5 fishing - 3	coal - 1 agriculture - 4	
CULTURES			Section Score	
17	Does your child know where certain resources may or may not be located?	oil - 3 lumber - 5 fishing - 1 coal - 4 agriculture - 2		
18	Does your child understand that one must dress for the climate?	sari - 3 fur-lined parka - 4 African tunic - 2 Aborigine loin cloth - 1		
19	Does your child understand that each country produces a different product?	jewelry - 2 vehicles - 4 machines - 5 personal computers - 1 transportation equipment - 3		
20	Is your child aware that different foods are eaten around the world?	corn - 2 rice - 4 wheat - 1 potatoes - 5 beets - 3		

45

Science

#	Assess	Answer	Notes	✓
PHYSICS			Section Score	
1	Does your child know that vertebrates have spines and internal skeletons?	cat - V chicken - V spider - I clam - I ladybug - I		
2	Does your child understand that warm-blooded animals have a constant body temperature but cold-blooded animals do not?	frog - C snake - C sheep - W shark - C parrot - W		
3	Does your child know the basic characteristics of different types of animals?	amphibian - 5 fish - 3 mammal - 1 insect - 6 bird - 2 reptile - 4		
4	Does your child understand that insects can be grouped in different orders?	assassin bug - 4 Goliath beetle - 1 house fly - 5 grasshopper - 3 moth - 2		
HUMAN BODY			Section Score	
5	Does your child understand what muscles do?	involuntary muscle - 2 cardiac muscle - 4 voluntary muscle - 1 skeletal muscle - 3		
6	Does your child know some of the major bones of the body?	femur / thigh bone - 5 humerus / arm bone - 3 ribs - 2 pelvis / hip - 4 sternum / breastbone - 1		
7	Does your child understand how an eye works?	optic nerve - 5 cornea - 1 pupil - 2 retina - 4 lens - 3		
8	Does your child understand how the ear works?	ear drum - 3 auditory nerve - 4 outer ear - 1 ear canal - 2		
ENERGY, HEAT, AND ENERGY TRANSFER			Section Score	
9	Is your child aware that light can pass through some objects but not others?	clear glass - T water - T aluminum foil - O wood - O		

STUDENT PLACEMENT TEST GUIDE

#	Assess	Answer	Notes	✔
10	Does your child understand that light travels in waves?	a		
11	Does you child understand that mirrors and lenses can bend light?	concave mirror - C convex mirror - A concave lens - B convex lens - D		
12	Does your child know the colors of the rainbow?	1. Red 2. Orange 3. Yellow 4. Green 5. Blue 6. Violet		
FOREST			Section Score	
13	Does your child understand that sound is caused by air vibrating?	c		
14	Does you child understand that sound waves can pass through solids, liquids, and gases?	d		
15	Does your child know what pitch and volume are?	b		
16	Does your child understand how vocal cords work?	Acceptable answer include: the voicebox, the larynx, air rushing by the vocal cords		
ASTRONOMY			Section Score	
17	Does your child know some of the planets and moons of our solar system?	Saturn - 6 Earth - 3 Neptune - 8 Mercury - 1 Venus - 2 Uranus - 7 Mars - 4 Jupiter - 5		
18	Does your child know that the universe includes all galaxies and star systems?	a		
19	Is your child familiar with how space is explored?	space shuttle - 3 space probe - 2 satellite - 4 telescope - 1		
20	Is your child familiar with some stars and constellations?	The Big Dipper - 3 The Little Dipper - 5 Orion - 4 Taurus - 1 Gemini - 2		

STUDENT PLACEMENT TEST GUIDE

#	Assess	Answer	Notes	✓
BIBLE STORIES			Section Score	
1	Does your child think carefully about what King David did?		becomes friends with Jonathan plays the harp for King Saul uses a slingshot to defeat Goliath becomes king of Israel	
2	Does your child understand that Mary and Martha were friends of Jesus?	b.		
3	Does your child understand the the Gospel is for the Gentiles as well as the Jews?		Acceptable answers include: Cornelius worshiped God. Cornelius asked Peter to come visit him. Peter saw a vision about unclean animals. Peter went to Cornelius to tell him about Jesus.	
4	Does your child understand the significance of the crucifixion?	crucifixion - 4 arrest - 2 burial - 5	trial - 3 betrayal - 1 resurrection - 6	
BIBLE REFERENCE TOOLS			Section Score	
5	Does your child know which books are Old and New Testament	Matthew - 4 Genesis - 1 Revelation - 6	Daniel - 3 Psalms - 2 Acts - 5	
6	Does your child know that the Bible has many types of literature?	Joshua - 2 Luke - 4 Romans - 5	Proverbs - 3 Exodus - 1	
7	Does your child know that the cross-reference gives other passages on the same topic?			
8	Does your child understand that footnotes are man's thoughts?			

For rows 7 and 8, the Notes column contains a reproduced Bible page:

51   GENESIS 1:28

16 j Jer. 31:35
21 m Ps. 104:25, 26
22 n ch. 8:17; 9:1
26 o ch. 3:22; 11:7; Isa. 6:8
p ch. 5:1; 9:6; 1 Cor. 11:7;
Eph. 4:24; Col. 3:10;
James 3:9 q ch. 9:2; Ps.
8:6-8; James 3:7
27 r ch. 2:18, 21-23; 5:2;
Mal. 2:15; Matt. 19:4;
Mark 10:6
28 s ch. 9:1, 7

light to rule the night—and the stars. [17] And God set them in the expanse of the heavens to give light on the earth, [18] to j rule over the day and over the night, and to separate the light from the darkness. And God saw that it was good. [19] And there was evening and there was morning, the fourth day.

[20] And God said, "Let the waters swarm with swarms of living creatures, and let birds [1] fly above the earth across the expanse of the heavens." [21] So m God created the great sea creatures and every living creature that moves, with which the waters swarm, according to their kinds, and every winged bird according to its kind. And God saw that it was good. [22] And God blessed them, saying, n "Be fruitful and multiply and fill the waters in the seas, and let birds multiply on the earth." [23] And there was evening and there was morning, the fifth day.

[24] And God said, "Let the earth bring forth living creatures according to their kinds— livestock and creeping things and beasts of the earth according to their kinds." And it was so. [25] And God made the beasts of the earth according to their kinds and the livestock according to their kinds, and everything that creeps on the ground according to its kind. And God saw that it was good.

[26] Then God said, o "Let us make man [2] in our image, p after our likeness. And q let them have dominion over the fish of the sea and over the birds of the heavens and over the livestock and over all the earth and over every creeping thing that creeps on the earth."

[27]   So God created man in his own image,
            in the image of God he created him;
            r male and female he created them.

[28] And God blessed them. And God said to them, s "Be fruitful and multiply and fill the

[1] Or flying things; see Leviticus 11:19-20 [2] The Hebrew word for man (adam) is the generic term for mankind and becomes the proper name Adam

...Isa. 40:25–26) is mentioned here only in a brief phrase, almost as if it were an afterthought. The focus of Genesis 1 is on the earth; the focus of the rest of the Bible is on man (male and female) as the pinnacle of God's creation and the object of his great salvation.

man is not made in the image of angels, nor is there any indication that angels participated in the creation of human beings. Many Christians and some Jews have taken "us" to be God speaking to himself, since God alone does the making in Gen. 1:27 (cf. 5:1); this would be the first hint of the

STUDENT PLACEMENT TEST GUIDE

#	Assess	Answer	Notes	✔
BIBLE PASSAGES			Section Score	
9	Does your child know what it means to trust, acknowledge, and submit?	Lord; heart; understanding; ways; straight		
10	Does your child understand what praising the Lord involves?	joy; earth; Lord; joyful songs		
11	Does your child understand that Jesus is our shepherd?	shepherd; nothing; lie; waters; refreshes; right		
12	Does your child understand that the 10 Commandments show us our sinful state?	gods; Me; make; image; misuse; name; Sabbath; father; mother; murder; adultery; steal; false; covet		
THEOLOGY			Section Score	
13	Can your child explain how God is in control?	c.		
14	Is your child able to give practical examples of how to obey God?	obeying mom and dad obeying teachers being kind to others		
15	Does your child understand that judgment awaits those that do not love and obey Jesus?	true		
16	Does your child say that he or she loves others and show love by being kind?	Acceptable answers include: giving hugs, helping others, giving gifts, telling someone you love them, doing fun things together		
CHURCH HISTORY AND MISSIONS			Section Score	
17	Does your child recognize the names of reformers and church fathers?	a.		
18		b.		
19		Johannes Hus John Calvin Peter Waldo		
20		c.		

Notes

MATH

Score	Section
	Numbers to 999,999
	Math Facts
	Measurement
	Fractions & Decimals
	Money

Total Score

Grade Placement

LANGUAGE ARTS

Score	Section
	Reading and Comprehension
	Writing
	Spelling & Vocabulary
	Grammar & Usage
	Literature

Total Score

Grade Placement

HISTORY & GEOGRAPHY

Score	Section
	World History
	World Geography
	United States History
	United States Geography
	Culture

Total Score

Grade Placement

SCIENCE

Score	Section
	Animal Classification
	Human Body
	Light & Optics
	Sound
	Astronomy

Total Score

Grade Placement

BIBLE

Score	Section
	Bible Stories
	Bible Reference Tools
	Bible Passages
	Theology
	Church History and Missions

Total Score

Grade Placement

STUDENT PLACEMENT SCORING

The Well Planned Start was designed to assess a grade level *per subject.* Use the key below to *determine the grade level for each subject.*

1. Each correct answer is valued at 1 point. Count the number in each section. Write the number in the score box to the left of the section.

2. Add the section scores together and place the total in the **Total Score** box.

3. Using the key below, determine the grade assessment for *each subject.*

SUBJECT TEST KEY

- Total Score = 20: Administer the 4th grade test for this subject. Your child may be ready for 5th grade.
- Total Score = 15-19: Your child is ready for the 4th grade.
- Total Score = 10-14: Base your decision on the following **section scores.**
  - Score 2 or less in 1-2 sections: Your child is ready for the 4th grade in this subject, but you can expect to give extra help throughout the year.
  - Score 2 or less in 3-5 sections: Your child should begin this subject at a 3rd grade level.
- All sections = 0-9: Administer the 2nd grade test for this subject. Your child needs additional evaluation.

BIBLE EXCEPTION

Because the development of spiritual growth is not confined to a grade level, the Bible tests for Well Planned Start were designed to cover a range through the following stages of education:

- Starting Out - Preschool - 1st Grade
- Getting Exciting: 2nd - 4th Grade
- Beginning to Understand: 5th - 8th Grade
- Learning to Reason: 9th - 12th Grade

When scoring Bible and determining placement, it is recommended to use your discretion in deciding if additional testing is needed or more time studying the topics covered.

WHAT NEXT?

Compare your findings to the parent assessment test and begin to make a plan of action on the following page.

If you suspect a learning challenge or special needs, we strongly recommend additional testing with a specialist.

MATH

grade

_____
_____
_____
_____
_____
_____
_____

LANGUAGE ARTS

grade

_____
_____
_____
_____
_____
_____
_____

HISTORY & GEOGRAPHY

grade

_____
_____
_____
_____
_____
_____
_____

SCIENCE

_____
_____
_____
_____
_____
_____
_____

BIBLE

_____
_____
_____
_____
_____
_____
_____

PLAN OF ACTION

Your child has completed the test, the scores are tallied, and a grade level is determined. But, it doesn't stop there! Here are some ways to utilize the information gleaned from this assessment to help you and your child tackle the new school year with confidence!

HOMESCHOOL

Use this space to note your child's grade level, gaps you observed during testing, areas where your child excels, and specific strategies you will be seeking as you choose curriculum. Make a list of academic needs for the coming year, and have that list on hand to check against the content in your curricula of choice.

HYBRIDS: CO-OP, TUTORIAL, & ENRICHMENTS

If your child is involved in homeschool classes taught through a co-op, use this area to note learning needs to discuss with your child's teacher(s). Also, make note of any enrichment activities you can do with your child to fill in gaps and strengthen weaknesses.

TRADITIONAL SCHOOL

If your child attends a private or public school, make note of areas you want to discuss with your child's teacher(s) to determine how to strengthen weaknesses. At home, plan trips or organize evening discussion to cater to strengths and incorporate Bible training.

STAGES OF EDUCATION (2ND - 4TH GRADE)
GETTING EXCITED

3rd grade
PARENT TEACHING TIPS

It is so much fun to watch the enthusiasm and excitement build as children begin elementary school. But, how do we keep that excitement burning in our young learners? An important reality to remember is that these early academic years are not intended to be processing years. They are, instead, collection years. Just as in the Starting Out stage, it is imperative that we continue to encourage exploration and absorption in a fun manner.

The excitement stage of learning will, naturally, start to see an implementation of targeted learning tools such as flashcards and learning games, as well as a few workbooks for writing and math. Here are a few practical ways to introduce those tools while still maintaining the enthusiasm of the Getting Excited stage:

1. Continue to vary learning experiences. Take field trips. Let science be fun exploration instead of the reading of textbooks. Use plays, puppet shows, international foods, and dress-up to teach social studies. Adopt a missionary or an unreached people group. Play games. Some subjects do require an introduction to workbooks. For everything else, though, find a way to teach through hands-on activities, picture books, living books, and games.

2. Explore. If your child shows an interest in a specific topic, explore more deeply. In later years, academic depth will become more important, and time to explore will have to be more targeted. So, for now, enjoy wide exploration.

3. Keep on reading. The importance of reading aloud together does not diminish during these early elementary years. If anything, it only increases! By reading aloud with your child, you not only reinforce a love of books. You also strengthen your child's early reading abilities (even if she is slow to read on her own!), continue nurturing a bond through a mutual love of stories, and introduce foundational concepts through the powerful medium of literature.

4. As you process through this stage, you begin to use the building blocks you started storing in the Starting Out stage.

In the following pages you will find practical teaching tips and activity suggestions for every concept covered in the placement test. Here are some ways to utilize these tips:

1. Use the suggested activities to strengthen low-scoring areas.

2. For strong areas, focus on activities that will keep your child challenged.

3. At times, having a negative experience with academics can take the joy out of learning. Restore that joy gently by choosing activities that will be fun for your child.

4. Use enrichment activities to put together a "summer camp." This is the perfect time to fill in gaps and bring kids up to grade level.

5. If you are homeschooling, utilize some of these activities on days that are too interrupted or chaotic for the normal school schedule. You can also use them for a relaxed "Friday Fun Day!"

6. Liven up a co-op class by incorporating some of these activities.

PARENT TEACHING TIPS

To use throughout the entire year!

Math

NUMBERS TO 999,999

- Practice writing numbers in Roman Numerals.

- Give your child six random digits and have him or her rearrange them to make the highest and lowest numbers possible.

- Write <,>, and = on index cards. Now write two numbers on a piece of paper and have your child place the correct symbol between them.

MATH FACTS

- Use flashcards or an app to practice math facts.

- Play math facts war. Lay down two cards and add, subtract, multiply, or divide. The highest answer wins.

- Print worksheets or get a workbook for extra practice.

- Rework incorrect problems together.

- Have an older sibling, family member, or friend explain difficult concepts.

MEASUREMENT

- Have your child double check answers before turning them in.

- Practice drawing lines and shapes.

- Go to the kitchen and find different containers of liquid. Read their quantities and arrange them in order from smallest to largest.

- Get a thermometer and read the temperature at different times of the day.

- Have your child help create a family daily schedule to practice time and clock skills.

FRACTIONS & DECIMALS

- Cut pizza pan-sized fractions out of poster board and practice comparing them.

- See if your child can write his or her own story problems.

- Have your child use measuring cups regularly to become familiar with the concept of fractions.

UNDERSTANDING MONEY

- Let your child use your money to pay for something at the store.

- Give your child play money to use in exchange for snacks and TV or electronics time to practice paying for items.

- If your child wants to buy something, have him handle interacting with the cashier with your supervision.

- Practice figuring change using play or real money.

JOURNAL YOUR EFFORTS

If you feel that your child is extremely behind, consider formal testing for a learning difficulty such as dyscalculia.

Language Arts

JOURNAL YOUR EFFORTS

READING & COMPREHENSION

- Take turns reading out loud
- Ask questions before, during, and after reading.
- Allow your child to read for a few minutes before lights out.
- Leave interesting books lying around the house for your child to find.

WRITING

- Encourage your child to go over his or her own work before turning it in.
- Let your child write a report about something and share it at a family gathering.
- Take a piece of your child's writing and let him or her find the subjects and verbs.
- Help your child research his or her interests at the library.
- Attend a writing workshop at the library.

SPELLING & VOCABULARY

- Get some word board games and have a family game night.
- Get a subscription to a magazine for vocabulary expansion.
- While reading, help your child look up new words in a dictionary.

GRAMMAR & USAGE

- Identify nouns and verbs in everyday reading, writing, and even speaking.
- When your child asks a question, show him or her how to find the answer.
- Study Greek and Latin roots.
- Look through a passage from a book and find the pronouns and antecedents.

LITERATURE

- Get your child a library card.
- Ask the children's librarian for a book list.
- Watch some film versions of classic books.
- Ask the children's librarian for a tour.
- Join the summer reading program at your library.

If you feel that your child is extremely behind, consider formal testing for a learning difficulty such as dyslexia or dysgraphia.

UNITED STATES HISTORY

- Make a chart of the differences among the thirteen colonies.
- Talk about your family's history.
- Go to a museum.
- Make a family scrapbook.
- Make a family tree.

UNITED STATES GEOGRAPHY

- Get some geography games or puzzles.
- Make a map of your town.
- Show your child how to use a compass.
- Collect quarters for each state.

CULTURE

- Study your region's history.
- While on vacation, sample local food and culture.
- Tell your child why you celebrate different days.
- Help your child research a certain area of the world.
- Shop the international aisle at the grocery store.

WORLD HISTORY

- Make a timeline.
- Act out a famous historical event.
- Make a model of a historical place or object.
- Choose a historical topic to discuss over dinner.
- Compare life in the past with life today.

WORLD GEOGRAPHY

- Get a globe.
- Put a map on the dining room table and cover it with a clear table cloth.
- Print some maps or get a workbook for extra practice.
- Read historical fiction and biographies out loud and map the locations you read about.
- Create a collage of a different country.

JOURNAL YOUR EFFORTS

Science

ANIMAL CLASSIFICATION

- When your child asks a question, ask him or her what he or she thinks. Then find the answer together.
- Visit the zoo and pay attention to the way the animals you see are classified.
- Assign a sibling to work with your child on a science project.
- Raise some tadpoles, butterflies, or ants.
- Read books about animals and discuss their characteristics.

HUMAN BODY

- Get a model of the human skeleton.
- Find a book that has overlays for the various body systems.
- Purchase a blood type kit and test the whole family.
- Consider scheduling an optometrist appointment for your child, or take him with you for yours. Ask questions.

LIGHT & OPTICS

- Let your child play with flashlights, laser pointers, and prisms.
- Get a subscription to a science or nature magazine.
- Borrow a library book with mirror and lens experiment suggestions.
- Find different objects that serve as prisms.

SOUND

- Make instruments out of household objects.
- Find a model of the ear and/or vocal chords.
- Experiment with the Doppler effect or pay attention to sounds while traveling.
- Place uncooked rice on a drum head and see how various sounds affect whether or not the rice moves.

ASTRONOMY

- Get a star chart and locate constellations.
- Make a model of the solar system.
- Watch videos of astronauts in space.
- Visit a planetarium or science museum.

Bible

BIBLE STORIES

- Take turns reading the Bible out loud together in a translation that is easy to understand.

- Make a Bible timeline.

BIBLE REFERENCE TOOLS

- Find some songs to help memorize the books of the Bible.

- Write the books of the Bible on different slips of paper and categorize them by type of book.

- Practice looking up a verse in the Bible and then looking up each cross-referenced verse.

BIBLE PASSAGES

- Give your child a good study Bible complete with a Bible cover and highlighter.

- Sing some Bible memorization songs.

- Read the Psalms and Proverbs of the day.

- Read the same passages over and over.

THEOLOGY

- Study your pastor's sermon passage in depth the following week. Take turns reading the Bible out loud together in a translation that is easy to understand.

- When trials come, talk about how God is in control of everything.

- Explain that obeying parents and teachers is the same as obeying God.

- Do not shelter your child from death. Talk about what will happen after we die.

- Praise your child for showing love to friends, family, and God.

CHURCH HISTORY & MISSIONS

- Read some biographies of church leaders.

- Talk about major events in church history.

- Ask your church leadership to teach on your denomination's heritage.

MILESTONES
WHAT TO EXPECT

The timely development of a child is a frequent question and concern among both new and experienced parents. In the following pages you will discover the physical, emotional, and academic development you can expect from your child **by the end of 3rd grade**.

The goal of the Well Planned Gal milestones is to have the information on hand as a guideline. These ranges of development can greatly aid you as you parent, teach, and train your child to the next level.

It is important, however, that you do not use these milestones to "diagnose" your child as behind or gifted. It is perfectly normal for children to display a broad range of abilities as they grow and develop.

Many things may influence a child's growth and development, including temporary stress, nutrition, illness, sleep habits, premature birth, learning styles, and physical growth spurts. If you have specific concerns or questions concerning your child's physical or academic progress, we urge you to consult your child's pediatrician.

The Well Planned Gal milestones are outlined in three ranges of growth and maturity.

YOUR CHILD SHOULD BE ABLE TO . . .

This area presents what **most** children this age are comfortable doing. Approximately 80% of children fall into this category.

YOUR CHILD MAY BE ABLE TO . . .

This area presents what **many** children this age are comfortable doing. Approximately 50% of children fall into this category.

YOUR CHILD MAY EVEN TRY TO . . .

This area presents what **some** children this age attempt. Approximately 20% of children -- including gifted or exceptional children -- fall into this category.

3rd grade

USING MILESTONES

Children usually fall into the Getting Excited stage in the 2nd through 4th grades, ranging in age from 7 to 11. While these early elementary years are a time of rapid growth, each child develops and learns at a unique pace. Your child may steadily grow physically and academically these years, or you may notice plateaus with definite growth spurts. Expect physical and mental growth to happen at different times, and be patient waiting for your child to be ready for the next step.

The elementary years are some of the most fun times for your family, as your child's personality becomes pronounced and he develops clear interests. Repress the urge to compare your child to his friends, and instead focus on what excites, motivates, and encourages his unique development.

Academics will begin to play a strong role in every aspect of your child's growth during this stage, but be sure to continue to incorporate a great deal of play into each day as you help your children achieve these milestones.

3RD GRADE MILESTONES

Understanding your child's growth

HOW YOUR CHILD IS GROWING

Date	✓	Milestone	Journal
Your child should be able to			
	☐	Play sports with increasing stamina	
	☐	Lift heavier objects	
	☐	Become more daring in outdoor play (watch out for tree climbing, heavy object throwing, and mock sword fights!)	
Your child may be able to			
	☐	Play team sports	
	☐	Become completely responsible for his own personal hygiene and grooming	
	☐	Use tools with supervision	
	☐	Enjoy making things	
Your child may even be able to			
	☐	Demonstrate clear handwriting	
	☐	Become more creative with artwork and crafts	
How you can help. You can encourage his growth through these milestones with activities like these:			
	☐	Consider a family fitness program	
	☐	Enroll in organized sports or martial arts	
	☐	Provide opportunities to climb on playground equipment	
	☐	Provide craft supplies, idea books, and instructional DVDs	

HOW YOUR CHILD IS FEELING

Date	✓	Milestone	Journal
Your child should			
	☐	Need special attention from his mother	
	☐	Become helpful and cheerful	
	☐	Appear at times to be overly dramatic or have quick mood changes	
	☐	Seem impatient	
	☐	Make friends more easily and choose a few very close friends	
	☐	Desire to participate in group activities	
	☐	Respond to peer pressure	
	☐	Understand money	
Your child may			
	☐	Better control his anger	
	☐	Form solid friendships	
	☐	Demonstrate empathy	
	☐	Overcome childhood fears	
	☐	Become stressed by common things like routine changes and assignments	
	☐	Begin to wonder about relationships with the opposite sex	
Your child may even			
	☐	Have a best friend	

	☐	Converse comfortably with all ages	
	☐	Speak and behave in public with maturity -- at rare times.	

How you can help. You can encourage his growth through these milestones with activities like these:

	☐	Set aside special one-on-one time.	
	☐	Ask child to help with special projects.	
	☐	Model appropriate ways to express emotions.	
	☐	Invite playmates over.	
	☐	Play games that require turns.	
	☐	Provide opportunities to earn spending money.	

Notes

HOW YOUR CHILD IS LEARNING

Date	✓	Milestone	Journal
Your child should be able to			
	☐	Converse comfortably with adults	
	☐	Enjoy reading independently	
	☐	Ask "why" questions frequently	
	☐	Understand reversibility and mentally rotate objects	
	☐	Write a paragraph with help	
	☐	Look up a word in a dictionary	
	☐	Identify basic parts of speech (noun, verb, modifier)	
	☐	Begin to grasp geography and identify continents, oceans, rivers, and mountain ranges	
	☐	Skip count by 10s, 5s, or 2s	
	☐	Use a number line	
	☐	Correctly compare simple fractions	
	☐	Recognize dollar bills and coins by name and amount	
	☐	Master addition and subtraction facts	
	☐	Measure with standard units	
	☐	Discuss the cycles of nature	
	☐	Grasp scientific classification (recognize the difference between an insect and a spider, a fish and a mammal)	
	☐	Identify simple machines	

Your child may be able to			
	☐	Plan and complete extensive projects	
	☐	Categorize things	
	☐	Read chapter books	
	☐	Conduct research	
	☐	Write brief compositions of more than one paragraph	
	☐	Spell more accurately	
	☐	Understand sentence structure and parts of speech	
	☐	Use a map and globe	
	☐	Round numbers	
	☐	Become familiar with Roman numerals	
	☐	Understand decimals and fractions	
	☐	Make change	
	☐	Add and subtract 2-digit numbers	
	☐	Master multiplication and division facts	
	☐	Convert some units of measure	
	☐	Understand area and perimeter	
	☐	Classify animals	
	☐	Know some body systems	
	☐	Comprehend the behavior of light and sound	
	☐	Understand ecosystems	
	☐	Name heavenly bodies	

HOW YOUR CHILD IS LEARNING

Date	✓	Milestone	Journal
Your child may even be able to			
	☐	Read longer chapter books for pleasure	
	☐	Write stories	
	☐	Begin long division	
	☐	Understand square roots and factoring	
	☐	Convert fractions to decimals	
	☐	Compare metric and American measurements	
	☐	Estimate	
	☐	Draw geometric shapes	
	☐	Write in cursive	
	☐	Write summaries and reports utilizing the writing process	
	☐	Grasp homophones	
	☐	Understand parts of speech and punctuation	
	☐	Identify major mountain ranges and bodies of water	
	☐	Appreciate the importance of a healthy lifestyle	
	☐	Understand atoms	
	☐	Comprehend electricity	
	☐	Identify geologic formations	
	☐	Understand basic meteorology	

CPSIA information can be obtained
at www.ICGtesting.com
Printed in the USA
LVHW021352090621
689659LV00001B/2